Pocket answer section for
SQA Intermediate 2 Biology
2003–2007

© 2007 Scottish Qualifications Authority, All Rights Reserved
Published by Leckie & Leckie Ltd, 3rd Floor, 4 Queen Street, Edinburgh EH2 1JE
tel: 0131 220 6831, fax: 0131 225 9987, enquiries@leckieandleckie.co.uk, www.leckieandleckie.co.uk

Biology Intermediate 2
2003

Section A

1.	C	14.	B
2.	D	15.	B
3.	A	16.	D
4.	B	17.	C
5.	B	18.	B
6.	C	19.	D
7.	D	20.	D
8.	A	21.	A
9.	C	22.	C
10.	C	23.	C
11.	A	24.	D
12.	B	25.	C
13.	A		

Section B

1. (a) (i) C (cytoplasm) and E (nucleus)

   (ii) photosynthesis/carbon fixation/Calvin cycle

   (b) DNA (deoxyribonucleic acid)

2. (a) Diffusion

   Carbon dioxide moves from a high concentration to a low concentration/moves down a concentration gradient

   (b) To prevent toxic build up/to prevent the cell from becoming acidic/to prevent the lowering of cell pH/carbon dioxide is a poison (in excess)

   (c) (aerobic) respiration

3. (a) (i) A
          B

   (ii) Osmosis

   (iii) turgid

   (b) (cell) wall

   (c) they shrink in size/crenated/crinkled edge

   (d) phosphorylase

4. (a) (i)

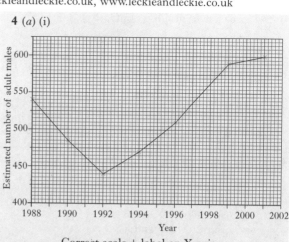

Correct scale + label on X axis
7 points plotted correctly + all joined by a line

(a) (ii) (population) increased/number of adult males increased

(b)

Activity	Effect on Biodiversity
pollution **over** hunting **over** fishing deforestation/habitat destruction	decrease in **species** numbers/extinction
setting up SSSIs/ conservation areas	increase in **species** numbers

Effect on biodiversity: decrease or increase and must relate to an increase or decrease in species numbers/or relate to extinction/dies out

(c) B

(d)

Adaptation	Explanation
spines instead of leaves	reduces surface area for evaporation
leaves have a thick cuticle	to prevent/reduce evaporation
presence of succulent tissue	plant can store water
presence of long roots	can reach deep underground water
presence of superficial roots	can absorb surface water

Biology Intermediate 2
2003 (cont.)

5. (a) Any **one** from:
temperature/concentration of salt water/pH/
size of petri dish/light (intensity)

(b) To acclimatise/adjust/adapt/get used to (new)
conditions/surroundings

(c) (i) They move towards the light

(ii) They feed on **plants** (which are found in
the light)

(d) Repeat/use more/different brine shrimps

6. (a) (i) Parent 1 = NN   Parent 2 = FF
(must use letters N and F)

(ii) first row of punnet square N and F
second row NN and NF
third row NF and FF

(iii) 1 : 2 : 1

(b) heterozygous
recessive
monohybrid

(c) polygenic

7. (a) 1.

Effect on population	Reason
increases	more animal and plant plankton available as food
decreases	less food for dog whelks – so they will eat more barnacles
stays the same	although more predation than by dog whelks, there is more animal and plant plankton for them to eat

2.

Effect on population	Reason
decreases	fewer dog whelks means less food for crabs – so greater predation of periwinkles
decreases	more animal and plant plankton gives more barnacles, more dog whelks, more crabs, more predation of periwinkles
stays the same	no change in dog whelk population, no change in number of crabs – predation of periwinkles remains the same

(b) A lot of algae are required to **feed** one limpet/
not all the energy is passed on at each stage/
energy is lost

(c) (i) Energy is lost as heat/during movement/in
undigested material/during respiration/in
uneaten material

(c) (ii)

Energy value (kJ/m²/year)	Niche	Named organism
100 000	**producer**	**plant plankton**
17000	primary consumer	animal plankton
1700	**secondary consumer**	dog whelks

8. (a)

Improvement	Explanation
decrease in height of stem	less chance of being blown over/easier to harvest
increase in grain **yield**	better financially/more food available/less land needed

(b) Takes a long time/improved characteristics are
not guaranteed/some characteristics may be
lost/enhances bad characteristics

(c) (i) Insulin/(human) growth hormone/
somatotrophin

(ii) **Step 2**
First box: Piece of a chromosome/Gene cut
out/removed

Second box: Plasmid extracted/cut open

Step 3
Piece of a chromosome/Gene inserted/
sealed into plasmid

Step 4
Gene/Plasmid inserted into bacterial cell/
host cell

9. (a) (i) To standardise results/as different numbers
were released/so a fair/valid comparison can
be made/to compare results

(ii) Light coloured are better camouflaged/
There is less predation of light coloured/
Fewer light coloured are eaten

(b) Natural selection

10. (a) (i)

	Before exercise	During exercise	After exercise
Breathing rate (breaths/min)	20	from 20 to 35	from 35 to 40 to 20
Pulse rate (beats/min)	75	from 75 to 130	from 130 to 82

(ii) To deliver **more oxygen** to the muscles/
for movement

This is needed to produce **more energy**

(b) Lactic acid

(c) (i) alveoli/air sacs

(ii) In the **red** blood cells/as carboxyhaemoglobin/
by haemoglobin

(Dissolved in) the plasma/as carbonic acid/
as bicarbonate

(d) In the lungs haemoglobin combines with
oxygen at high oxygen levels

11. (a)

Name of area	Letter	Function
Sensory strip	**R**	Receives nerve impulses from the sense organs
Cerebellum	**S**	<u>controls</u> **balance**/ **(muscular) coordination**
Medulla	T	<u>controls</u> **heart rate**/ <u>controls</u> **breathing rate**

(b) Spinal cord

(c) Sensory

(d)

Statement	True	False	Correction
External temperature is detected by receptors in the <u>skin</u>.	✔		
The area of the brain which regulates body temperature is the <u>medulla</u>.		✔	**hypothalamus**
Blood vessels in the skin <u>constrict</u> in response to an increase in external temperature.		✔	**dilate**

Section C

1. A. Photosynthesis

Stage 1: Photolysis

This stage occurs in the chloroplasts in the presence of light/Chlorophyll is used to absorb light energy

Water is split to produce hydrogen and oxygen

The hydrogen combines with a hydrogen acceptor

The oxygen is given off as a by-product

Stage 2: Carbon Fixation

The hydrogen from photolysis combines with CO_2

This requires the ATP produced during photolysis

Glucose is produced

This stage is controlled by enzymes

B. Anaerobic respiration

The yeast provides the enzymes for the process

The grape juice contains the sugar/glucose

The first stage of anaerobic respiration is called glycolysis

In this stage sugar/glucose is broken down into pyruvic acid

2 ATP molecules are produced **per glucose molecule**

The second stage is a fermentation process

The pyruvic acid is broken down in the absence of oxygen

Carbon dioxide gas is given off

Alcohol is also produced

This is an irreversible reaction

2. A.
Arteries

Arteries have a **thick muscular** wall

They carry blood at high pressure

They have a narrow, central cavity

They carry blood away from the heart/They deliver blood to the organs/They carry oxygenated blood except for the pulmonary artery

Veins

Veins have a **thin muscular** wall

They carry blood at low pressure

They have a wide, central cavity

They carry blood back to the heart/They carry blood away from the organs/They carry deoxygenated blood except for the pulmonary vein

Capillaries

Capillaries have **very thin** walls/Their **walls** are 1 cell thick

They have a very narrow diameter

They allow for the exchange/diffusion of materials

They **link** arteries to veins

B.
Problem

The tissues of the fish are hypertonic to its surroundings/The freshwater is hypotonic to the tissues of the fish

Water passes from a high water concentration to a low water concentration

This process is called osmosis

Therefore water passes into the fish

The fish needs to remove this excess water

Mechanisms

Osmoregulation takes place

Excess water is removed by the kidney

A large volume of urine is produced

This urine is very dilute

Biology Intermediate 2
2004

Section A

1. C	2. A	3. B	4. D	5. B
6. C	7. B	8. B	9. C	10. C
11. C	12. A	13. A	14. D	15. A
16. D	17. C	18. B	19. D	20. D
21. D	22. A	23. D	24. B	25. A

Section B

1. (a) (i) Any two of the following:
   - Volume of starch/amylase/buffer/pH solution/
   - Concentration of starch/amylase/
   - Mass of starch/
   - Time/
   (ii) Benedicts/clinistix

   (b) (i) Any one of the following:
   - Amylase/enzyme breaks down starch at pH 7/neutral pH.
   - Neutral pH/pH 7 is optimum for amylase/enzyme/
   - Amylase/enzyme works best at pH7/neutral pH/
   (ii) Prediction:
   No simple sugars would be produced/
   or
   Negative reaction for simple sugars test
   Explanation:
   Enzyme/amylase has been denatured/inactive/
   or
   Active site has changed shape/

   (c) To produce small/soluble molecules/particles/
   To allow absorption/diffusion to occur into body/cells/blood/gut wall

2. (a) hypothalamus
   constrict
   decreases

   (b) (i) D B E A C
   (ii) For protection/defence/to prevent harm/hurt/damage/injury
   or
   They are rapid

3. (a) A = oesophagus/gullet
   B = duodenum/**small** intestine

   (b) Longitudinal/circular muscle

   (c) Any one of the following:
   - Churns/Mixes food **with** digestive juices/enzymes/acid
   - **Physical/mechanical** breakdown of food **into small pieces**
   - Breakdown of food is **faster**

4. (a)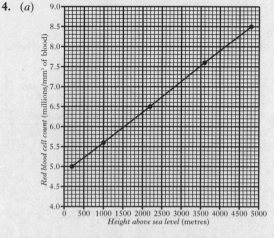

   (b) (i) As the height above sea level increases the red blood cell count increases
   (ii) It increases the chance of oxygen being picked up by the blood/haemoglobin at low oxygen concentrations/high altitude

5. (a) (i) Diffusion
   (ii) Carbon dioxide/waste (materials)
   (iii) (cell) membrane

   (b) To allow carbon dioxide to diffuse/move into the leaf cells
   Carbon dioxide required for photosynthesis/to produce food

6. (a) (i) Bacteria/lactobacillus
   (ii) Lactic acid
   (iii) To prevent bacteria/microbes (from the air) contaminating
   (iv) To check no bacteria are present in the milk/to show the change is not due to the milk.
   or
   To show that it was the yoghurt which brought about the change

   (b) (i) –1·4
   (ii) To increase reliability/to reduce effect of atypical results
   (iii) Any one of the following:
   - Contamination (from the air)
   - Milk not sterilised correctly
   - Yoghurt not boiled long enough

7. (a) (i) Slide A = cells would swell/burst/haemolyse
   Slide C = cells would shrink/be crenated
   (ii) Osmosis
   (iii) When two solutions have the same water **concentration**
   or
   It has the same water concentration **as the blood/cells**

7. (b) (i) Any one of the following:
- They become dehydrated/lose water
- They take in excess salt
- They have a **higher** water concentration/they are hypotonic to surroundings

(ii) Any one of the following:
- Sea water is drunk
- Small volume of/concentrated urine produced
- They excrete excess salt

8. (a) Glycolysis

(b) X= carbon dioxide, Y = oxygen

(c) Glucose

(d) ADP + Pi/inorganic phosphate

(e) Stage 1 = 2 or 4
Stage 2 = 36

(f) Heat

9. (a) (i) First box
Blaeberry (leaves/berries/stems)
or
Pine (needles/cones/trees)
or
Plants/vegetation

Second box
Capercaillie

Third box
Fox/wild cat/crow

(ii)

Term	Named Example
ecosystem	(Pine) forest
population	all the crows
herbivore	Capercaillie

(iii) The variety of species present (in an ecosystem)

(b) Any one of the following:
- Nests were destroyed/decreased vegetation for nesting
- Capercaillie competed (with deer/sheep) for food
- Less food/more competition

(c) Habitat destruction/pollution/deforestation/desertification/grazing/**over**fishing/**over**hunting

10. (a) (i) Gg
(ii) False Alleles
True
False Heterozygous
(iii) 4 : 1

10. (a) (continued)

(iv) Any one of the following:
- **Fertilisation** is a random/chance process
- Some fertilised eggs did not develop/die
- Numbers in sample are low

(b) Continuous
Discontinuous

(c) Any one of the following:
- Skin colour/hair colour/eye colour
- Weight/height
- Any feature showing continuous variation in humans

11. (a) Ovary   23
Testes   23
(b) (i) 2
(ii) meiosis
(iii)

(c) Any one of the following:
- Different types of **gametes/sex cells** are formed
- **Brings about/increases** variation in offspring/zygote
- **Increases** variation within a species
- **Increases** variation in phenotypes/genotypes

Section C

1. A. Any 3 from
(Right side of the heart to and from the lungs)
R1 X is the right atrium/blood starts in right atrium
R2 Blood goes to right ventricle
R3 Blood goes into the pulmonary artery
R4 Blood goes to the lungs
R5 Then back to the heart
R6 Through the pulmonary vein

Any 2 from
(Left side of heart)
L1 Blood enters the left atrium
L2 Blood goes to the left ventricle
L3 Blood goes to vessel Y/aorta
L4 Vessel Y is the aorta

Biology Intermediate 2
2004 (cont.)

1. B. Urine production in the nephrons
        Any 3 from
        (Filtration)
        F1 Blood enters the glomerulus
        F2 Filtration (of the blood) occurs
        F3 Ultrafiltration/High pressure in the
            glomerulus
        F4 Result of filtration/filtrate/filtered
            substances/water, glucose, urea (and
            salts)/(all) small molecules pass
        F5 into the Bowmans capsule/(kidney) tubule

    Any 3 from
        (Reabsorption)
        R1 Reabsorption occurs
        R2 Along the tubule
        R3 (Useful/reabsorbed/absorbed)
            substances/pass into the blood/capillary
        R4 Substances (re)absorbed are water, glucose
            and salts
        R5 Urea not (re)absorbed
        R6 Fluid left (after (re)absorption) is urine
        R7 (Urine) passes into the collecting duct
        R8 Urine contains urea, salts and water

2. A. Adaptations
        Any 3 from
        A1 Roots (very) long/deep (underground)
        A2 Roots—superficial
        A3 Small leaves/no leaves/needles/spines/
            spikes/thorns
        A4 Reduced surface area of plant/part
        A5 Leaves/stems have thick/waxy cuticle
        A6 Contain succulent tissue/water storage
            tissue

        Explanations
        Any 3—must link with correct adaptation
        E1 More chance of locating (deep) water
        E2 More chance of absorbing surface water
            (before it evaporates)
        E3 Reduces water loss/reduced SA/protection
            from animals
        E4 Reduces water loss
        E5 Reduces water loss
        E6 Stores water

2. B. Structure of chromosomes
        Any 3 from
        S1 Contain the genes/genetic code/genetic
            information
        S2 Composed of DNA
        S3 DNA is made up of nucleotides/bases/
            name 4 bases or ATGC
        S4 Bases in a chain/sequence
        S5 Chromosomes are composed of two
            chromatids/or **labelled** diagram showing
            these

        Explanation
        Any 3 from
        E1 Order of bases (is important/needed)
        E2 (To) determine the sequence of amino
            acids (in proteins)
        E3 This determines (the type of/shape
            of/structure) protein produced
        E4 and the properties of the protein/functions
            of protein
        E5 Proteins produced may be enzymes
        E6 or hormones
        E7 Proteins/enzymes/hormones/genes/genetic
            code/genetic information/determine
            characteristics/phenotype

Biology Intermediate 2
2005

Section A

1.	C	14.	D
2.	C	15.	C
3.	B	16.	C
4.	A	17.	D
5.	A	18.	D
6.	A	19.	A
7.	D	20.	B
8.	D	21.	C
9.	C	22.	D
10.	C	23.	C
11.	D	24.	A
12.	D	25.	A
13.	B		

Section B

1. (a)
   - A - Salivary gland
   - G - Gall bladder
   - E - Large intestine/colon

   (b)
   - F
   - B
   - C

   (c) Glycogen

2. (a) (i)• A - Carries blood to the kidney
   - B - Bladder - stores urine
   - C - urethra
   (ii) *Any one of:*
   - Vessel A has a higher oxygen conc
   - lower carbon dioxide conc
   - higher urea concentration
   - higher glucose conc
   - higher salt conc than B
   - A has oxygenated blood, B has deoxygenated blood
   - (a comparison must be made)

   (b) All glucose is reabsorbed **or** All glucose is absorbed into blood

   (c) (i) ADH **or** anti diuretic (hormone)
   (ii) Increases **or** decreases **or** changes the permeability of the tubules to water
   Makes them absorb more **or** less water

3. (a) 2:5
   (b)

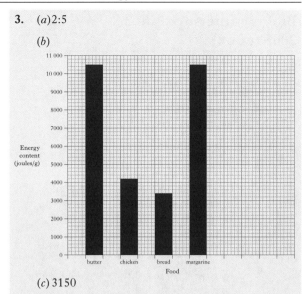

   (c) 3150
   (d) They have the same energy content **or** they have the same amount of energy.

4. (a) (i) Aorta
   (ii) Pulmonary artery
   (iii) Oxygen
   Glucose

   (b) (i) Lymphocyte
   (ii) *Any one of:*
   - An antibody is specific
   - it has a specific **or** complementary shape **or** structure
   - its shape fits the disease-causing organism
   (iii) Antibody production is faster after second injection or converse
   Antibody concentration is greater after second injection (e.g. "the second injection produced more antibodies") or converse

5. (a) (i) Diffusion
   (ii) *Any one of:*
   - For respiration
   - for energy
   - to produce ATP
   - to release energy
   (iii) High low
   (iv) Carbon dioxide

   (b) *Any two of:*
   - Thin wall **or** one cell thick lining **or** wall
   - Moist
   - Have a good blood supply **or** network of blood vessels
   - Large surface area **or** numerous

6. (a) (i) Synthesis
   (Potato) phosphorylase
   (ii) Any one of:

   (b) Protein

Biology Intermediate 2
2005 (cont.)

6. (c) *Any one of:*
   - It changes shape
   - becomes deformed
   - structure changes
   - it has altered shape

   (d) lowers energy input

7. (a) (i) *Any one of the following:*
   - Green algae → copepods → dragonfly larvae → trout
   - Green algae → copepods → damselfly larvae → trout
   - Green algae → copepods → dragonfly larvae → diving beetle
   - Duckweed → mayfly larvae → dragonfly larvae → diving beetle
   - Duckweed → mayfly larvae → damsel fly larvae → trout
   - Duckweed → mayfly larvae → dragonfly larvae → trout

   (ii) Copepods and mayfly larvae

   (iii) Any correct pyramid from the web with complete food chain
   e.g.

   (b) Organism **or** animal which eats plants and animals

   (c) Biodiversity

8. (a) (i) 15
   (ii) • As temperature increases up to 20°C **or** optimum temperature decomposition increases **and**
   • After 20°C **or** optimum temperature decomposition decreases

   (b) *Any one of:*
   - Enzymes
   - living organisms
   - decomposers
   - bacteria
   - fungi   } needed for decomposition
   - enzymes denatured at higher temperatures

   (c) (i) Bacteria **or** fungi
   (ii) *Any one of:*
   - Return nutrients to the soil
   - recycle nutrients
   - breakdown dead or decaying material
   - breakdown organic waste

9. (a)

Phenotype	Affected by genes	Affected by environment
Eye colour	✓	
Height	✓	✓
Blood group	✓	
Hand span	✓	✓

   (b) Continuous

   (c) Female
   Reasons could include:
   - Both sex chromosomes are the same type **or** same length **or** same shape **or** identical
   - Sex chromosomes not XY/no Y chromosome
   - Sex chromosome are XX

   (d) • Gametes
   • one set
   • fertilisation

10. (a) (i) Each dish should have labelled **or** drawn the same number of seeds per dish
   One dish with each percentage concentration of chemical (ie.0·1%; 1%; 10%) **or** indicate that they are all the same volume of chemical
   (ii) Check for signs of germination eg change in height **or** length **or** mass **or** root growth
   Count the number of seeds germinated (in a given time period)
   (iii) Same number of seeds as part (i) of question **and** water

   (b) *Any one of:*
   - Stops **or** reduces **or** no competition
   - an example (e.g. more nutrients available to black walnut trees)
   - better chance of survival

11. (a) A
   Beak is long OR narrow OR beak can easily extract insects (from rotting log)

   (b) • feed on different food
   • Found in different habitats

Section C

1A Any five from:
- Selective breeding
- Dogs have a variety of characteristics
- Any example(s) of characteristics
- Dogs selected to breed together
- Selection **or** breeding repeated many times
- Not always reliable **or** offspring do not always show desirable characteristics
- It takes a long time (to obtain a breed with the required characteristics)

1B Any five from:
- Natural selection
- Black form occurs naturally **or** by mutation
- (Pollution) causes trees to be coated with soot **or** to blacken **or** to change colour/lichen die
- Black form are better camouflaged **or** blend in better **or** hidden (not hide)
- Less chance of being eaten **or** seen by predators **or** more chance of survival
- Greater chance of passing black gene onto next generation **or** of breeding
- Greater number of black form in next generation
  (**Or** reverse of above for light form)

2A *Answers may include:*
- (Both processes involve) anaerobic respiration/fermentation

Maximum of three from:
- (Yoghurt cell type) bacteria
- (Yoghurt substrate) lactose/sugar in milk
- (Yoghurt product) lactic acid

Maximum of three from:
- (biogas cell type)   bacteria
- (biogas substrate)   organic waste
- (biogas product)   methane
- (gasohol cell type)   yeast
- (gasohol substrate)   sugar(cane)/glucose
- (gasohol product)   ethanol/alcohol
- (Gasohol) ethanol/alcohol + petrol = fuel /gasohol

2B *Any two from:*
- Carbon dioxide (concentration)
- Light (intensity)
- Temperature

Any three from:
- Changing these factors to an optimum level (for photosynthesis)
- By artificial lighting **or** additional heating **or** adding carbon dioxide
- (Rate of) photosynthesis is increased
- More glucose **or** food is available (for growth)

Biology Intermediate 2
2006

Section A

1. C	11. D	21. A
2. A	12. A	22. B
3. B	13. B	23. C
4. D	14. D	24. B
5. D	15. B	25. D
6. B	16. D	
7. A	17. C	
8. C	18. C	
9. A	19. B	
10. A	20. C	

Section B

1. (*a*) False bronchi/bronchus
   True
   True

   (*b*) (i) 0·8
   (ii) As (lung) pressure decreases/goes down the volume (of the air in the lungs) increases/goes up
   OR
   As volume of air (in the lungs) increases the lung pressure decreases.
   (iii) There is still 2·4L of air in the lungs (after breathing out)
   OR
   volume (of air in lungs) does not fall to 0

2. (*a*) (i) To prevent backflow (into the heart/atrium/ventricle)
   (ii) P and M
   (iii) (It would be) reduced
   Explanation – deoxygenated blood would (leak into left side of heart and) mix with oxygenated blood
   OR
   Some blood would be pumped around the body without going to the lungs.

   (*b*) (i) Renal artery   D
   Pulmonary vein   B
   (ii) Artery walls are thicker/more muscular
   OR
   lumen/bore/cavity smaller
   OR
   arteries do not contain valves, veins do or vice versa
   Must be a comparison

Biology Intermediate 2
2006 (cont.)

3. (*a*) (i) Maltose
   (ii) 35-40

   (*b*) (i) Specific/specificity
   (ii) Active site

4. (*a*) Fat – contains more than/twice as much energy
   (than carbohydrate and protein)
   Answer must be comparative

   (*b*) Lilac/purple/violet/mauve

   (*c*) Nitrogen

   (*d*) Calcium – formation/strengthening/repairing of
   bone/teeth/clotting of blood/contraction of
   muscles
   Iron – component of haemoglobin/forming red
   blood cells
   Role must be correct for the mineral named.

5. (*a*) (i) (Cell) membrane
   (ii) Controls cell's
   activities/function(s)/chemical reactions
   OR
   Stores/carries/contains genetic/
   chromosomal information or genes
   OR
   Passes on genetic/chromosomal
   information or genes
   OR
   Stores/carries/contains DNA

   (*b*) (i) P
   (ii) Turgid

   (*c*) (i) Bacteria
   (ii) Methane

6. (*a*) (i) 12·00/noon/midday
   (ii) 06·00 and 18·00 or any times in between

   (*b*) Chlorophyll

   (*c*) X = Carbon fixation/Calvin cycle
   Y = CO_2
   Z = cellulose

7. (*a*) (i) 17·5
   (ii) Start/Initial lengths were different
   OR
   to standardise
   OR
   To be valid/for validity
   (iii) To prevent cross contamination/to prevent
   contamination with liquids of different
   concentrations/mixing the different liquids

   (*b*) Cell division/protein synthesis/transmission of
   nerve impulses/glycolysis/growth/repair/heat
   production/active transport

8. (*a*) (i)

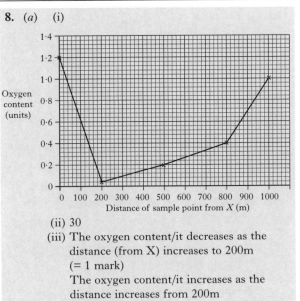

   (ii) 30
   (iii) The oxygen content/it decreases as the
   distance (from X) increases to 200m
   (= 1 mark)
   The oxygen content/it increases as the
   distance increases from 200m
   (= 1 mark)
   (iv) The large numbers of micro-organisms
   had used up the oxygen

   (*b*) It is reduced/decreased/lowered

9. (*a*) (i)

A	B	C
oak/tree	squirrel	owl
oak/tree	squirrel	fox
oak/tree	caterpillar	shrew

   (ii)

Producer   oak/tree/leaf (litter)/leaves
Predator   fox/owl/shrew/woodmouse
Decomposer   fungi
Herbivore   earthworm/squirrel/caterpillar

   (iii)

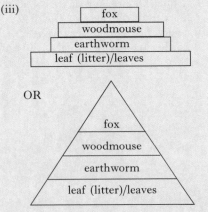

OR

   (*b*) Niche

10. (a) C A C B

(b) (5), 3, 2, 4, 1

(c) Produces large quantities of product
OR
increased range of products
OR
increased/quicker rate of production
OR
no allergic reaction to product
OR
produces desired characteristics
OR
produces medicines
OR
production costs lower

(d) Round shape/spines

11. (a) short
homozygous   heterozygous

(b) (i) Jamie – tongue roller
Ben – rr
(ii) 100
(iii) XX/both X

12. (a) (i)
A	testis cell	46
B	sperm	23
C	ova/ovum/egg	23
D	zygote/fertilised egg/ovum	46

(ii) The nuclei of the gametes fuse
OR
2 sets of chromosomes are restored

(b) (i) Chromosome(s)/gene(s)/chromatid(s)/
plasmid(s)
(ii) Determines the sequence of amino acids in
a protein/enzyme
OR
determines the structure/function/type of
a protein/enzyme

Section C

1.　A

Stage 1
Maximum of three from:
A1　enzyme controlled
A2　glucose (in context as raw material)
A3　converted to pyruvic acid
A4　glycolysis (in context)
A5　is anaerobic/oxygen not used
A6　energy is released
A7　2 ATP produced (per glucose molecule)

Stage 2
Maximum of three from:
B1　enzyme controlled (if A1 mark not already
awarded)
B2　energy released (if A6 mark not already
awarded)
B3　pyruvic acid
B4　broken down to carbon dioxide and water
B5　oxygen required/aerobic
B6　36 ATP produced/total of 38 ATP produced
(per glucose molecule)

(Total 5 marks)

1.　B

Process 1
Maximum of three from:
A1　diffusion
A2　movement of substance/molecules/glucose
from high to low concentration
OR
movement of a substance/molecules/glucose
down a concentration gradient
A3　glucose will move out (of tubing bag)
A4　starch will not move (out)
A5　glucose molecule small/starch molecule large
A6　membrane controls entry/exit

Process 2
Maximum of three from:
B1　osmosis
B2　movement/diffusion of water from high to
low concentration
OR
movement/diffusion of water down a
concentration gradient
B3　through a selectively permeable
membrane/semi permeable membrane
B4　water will move in (through the membrane)
B5　water is hypotonic to mixture
OR
mixture is hypertonic to water

(Total 5 marks)

2.　A

Role of small intestine in digestion
Maximum of three from:
A1　food is broken down into small, soluble
molecules
A2　Example of substrate and product eg fats,
fatty acids and glycerol
A3　produces/contains enzymes
A4　example of enzyme eg trypsin
A5　fats are emulsified (by bile)

Role of small intestine in absorption
Maximum of three from:
B1　movement/diffusion of soluble food/named
example/small molecules through the
(intestine) wall
B2　surface area is increased by being
long/folded/villi
B3　giving increased/more efficient absorption
B4　the lining of the small intestine is thin
OR
the lining of each villus is thin/one cell thick
B5　giving fast diffusion/absorption/ movement
B6　a villus contains a lacteal and
capillaries/capillary network
OR
labelled diagram showing these
B7　amino acids/glucose absorbed into the
blood/capillaries
B8　fatty acids and glycerol are absorbed into the
lacteal/lymphatic vessel

(Total 5 marks)

Biology Intermediate 2
2006 (cont.)

2. B

Role of hypothalamus
Maximum of three from:

A1   (osmo)receptors present in hypothalamus

A2   osmoreceptors/hypothalamus stimulated by a
        change in the water concentration of the
        blood
        OR
        osmoreceptors/hypothalamus detects/senses/
        monitors the water concentration of the blood

A3   a decrease/increase/change in water
        (concentration) causes an increase/decrease/
        change in production of ADH

A4   hypothalamus stimulates/communicates
        with/informs/sends a message to the pituitary
        gland

A5   pituitary produces/releases ADH

Role of ADH
Maximum of three from:

B1   ADH changes the permeability of the (kidney)
        tubules/collecting ducts

B2   an increase/decrease in ADH causes more/less
        water to be reabsorbed
        OR
        an increase/decrease in ADH causes more/less
        water to be absorbed/returned into blood

B3   water concentration (of the blood) increases/
        decreases/returns to normal

B4   concentration/volume of urine changes
        (increases/decreases – must match
        description)

B5   this is an example of negative feedback
                                    (Total 5 marks)

Biology Intermediate 2
2007

SECTION A

1.	C	**11.**	A	**21.**	D
2.	D	**12.**	B	**22.**	B
3.	A	**13.**	D	**23.**	C
4.	C	**14.**	B	**24.**	C
5.	B	**15.**	B	**25.**	B
6.	C	**16.**	D		
7.	D	**17.**	C		
8.	B	**18.**	A		
9.	D	**19.**	D		
10.	A	**20.**	A		

SECTION B

1. (*a*) trachea,
        artery, left

    (*b*) *Any two from:*
        • thin/one cell thick lining/wall
        • moist
        • large surface area
        • good blood supply **or** many blood
          capillaries **or** in close contact with blood
          capillaries

    (*c*) (i) glucose
         (ii) carbon dioxide/water/lactic acid

    (*d*) (i) water
         (ii) Turgid/hypertonic

2. (*a*) (i) • To make sure no other factor is
                producing the result **or**
              • to show it is the germinating/live peas
                that are producing the result **or**
              • to show it is the germinating/live peas
                that are using oxygen **or**
              • for a valid conclusion
            (ii) It/The liquid will rise more quickly/higher.

    (*b*)

Aerobic respiration in germinating peas	Anaerobic respiration in germinating peas
X Y	W X Z

3. (*a*) (i) green/yellow/orange/red/brown
            (ii) Protein

    (*b*) Box 1: amino acids
         Box 2: carbon, hydrogen, oxygen/CHO

    (*c*) (i) pepsin/rennin
            (ii) any value beween 1·4 to 1·6

4. (*a*) (i) 5·5
   (ii) • concentration of hydrogen peroxide **or**
        • pH (of hydrogen peroxide) **or**
        • mass/surface area/volume of tissue/cube **or**
        • temperature
   (iii) repeated (and average calculated)
   (iv) • different tissues have different catalase concentrations **or**
        • liver has the most catalase **or**
        • apple has the least catalase

   (*b*) (i) synthesis
   (ii) increases/speeds it up/faster
   (iii) • lipase not specific to glucose-1-phosphate **or**
        • lipase/active site does not fit glucose-1-phosphate **or**
        • lipase is specific to fats **or**
        • only phosphorylase is specific to glucose-1-phosphate **or**
        • an enzyme is specific to its substrate/reaction

5. (*a*)

Structure	Letter	Fuction
Bladder	E	**Stores/holds urine**
Renal artery	A	Carries blood into the kidney
Ureter	**D**	Carries urine away from the kidney

   (*b*) (i) ADH/anti diuretic (hormone)
   (ii) decreases/reduces/less
   (iii) glucose and salts
   (iv) 60

6. (*a*) P sensory
   Q motor

   (*b*) (eyelid) muscles

   (*c*) for protection or rapid/fast/quick

7. (*a*) (i) oxygen
   (ii) A NB Drawn line should not extend to the origin or past the last point.

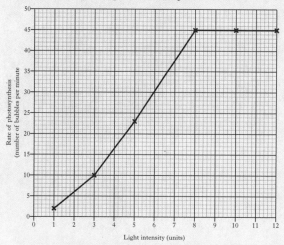

   B Another factor is limiting (photosynthesis)
   or
   It has reached the optimum/maximum rate for these conditions.

7. (*b*) (i) ATP
        hydrogen/NADPH$_2$
   (ii) carbon fixation/Calvin cycle

   (*c*)

Role of carbohydrate in plant cells	Name of carbohydrate
Storage as an insoluble material	**starch**
Forms cell walls	**cellulose**

8. (*a*) (i) nucleus
   (ii) A DNA/deoxyribonucleic acid
       B *Any two from:*
          It/DNA determines the sequence of amino acids in enzyme/protein **or**
          It/DNA determines the structure/function/type of enzyme/protein **or**
          Enzymes/proteins control cell activities.

   (*b*) (i) Meiosis
   (ii) Random/independent assortment
   (iii) Half,
        fusion, twice

9. (*a*) (i) (Cross) 1 /F_1
   (ii)

		Genotypes of gametes of Cross 2 single comb parent	
		r	r
Genotypes of gametes of Cross 2 rose comb parent	R	**Rr**	**Rr**
	r	**rr**	**rr**

   (*b*)

Statement	True	False	Correction
co-dominant		✓	polygenic
gene	✓		
homozygous	✓		

10. (*a*) Jan to Apr - decreases
   Apr to Aug - increases
   Aug to Dec - decreases
   Figure and unit used at least once (e.g. Jan = 6000/m^2)

   (*b*) 6

   (*c*) • No/fewer predators/birds from April to August **or**
        • They have reproduced from April to August

   (*d*) • Decreases:
          Corophium will become extinct **or** reduced number of Corophium leads to reduced number of predator species **or**
        • Stays the same:
          No species become extinct (only population falls) **or**
        • Increases:
          Less Corophium means less competition, therefore more species move in

Biology Intermediate 2
2007 (cont.)

SECTION C

1. **A** (a) A1   red blood cells and plasma

   (b) *Maximum of four from:*
   A2   oxygen transported in red blood cells
   A3   attached to haemoglobin/as oxyhaemoglobin
   A4   carbon dioxide transported in red blood cells/attached to haemoglobin
   A5   carbon dioxide carried in/dissolved in plasma
   A6   carried as bicarbonate ions
   A7   soluble foods dissolved in plasma
   A8   named example of soluble food carried
   A9   other correct substance carried by plasma, e.g. water, hormones, vitamins, minerals, salts, fats, proteins

1. **B** (a) B1   hypothalamus

   (b) *Maximum of four from:*
   B2   sweating is reduced/stops
   B3   blood vessels constrict/narrow/vasoconstriction
   B4   reduces blood flow (to skin)
   B5   to reduce heat loss
   B6   hair stands on end/hair (erector) muscles contract
   B7   to trap air/heat/insulate
   B8   rapid/quick/repeated muscle contraction/shivering
   B9   to generate heat/increase (body) temperature/heat up

2. **A** A1 (Insulin) gene identified/located
   A2 (Insulin) gene removed from human chromosome
   A3 Plasmid removed from bacterium
   A4 Plasmid cut open
   A5 Enzyme(s) used
   A6 (Insulin) gene inserted into plasmid
   A7 Plasmid inserted into bacterium
   A8 Bacteria multiply/cultured
   A9 Bacteria produce insulin
   A10 Insulin extracted/purified for use

2. **B** B1 Two forms found
   B2 Dark form occurs naturally/by mutation
   B3 In rural/non-polluted areas trees covered in lichen/light coloured
   B4 In industrial/polluted areas trees covered in soot/dark coloured
   B5 Example of which form is most/least common linked to its environment
   B6 Description of camouflage (**not** active, e.g. moths camouflage themselves)
   B7 Seen/eaten by predators/birds
   B8 Example of chances of survival
   B9 Example of chances of breeding
   B10 Example of chances of passing on their characteristics/genes to the next generation
   B11 Description of population change